Publisher
Robyn Moore

Color
Brian Miller

AbstractStudioComics.com

ISBN:978-1-892597-95-3

PARKER GIRLS
DEAD QUIET

BY

TERRY MOORE

TURKS AND CAICOS ISLANDS.

BURP

7

MAYBE, OR MAYBE I'VE SEEN YOU WALKING AROUND THE RESORT THIS WEEK LIKE A LOST LITTLE BOY AND I THINK YOU'RE CUTE.

NO ONE'S EVER SAID THAT TO ME BEFORE.

WELL I JUST DID... BUT YOU DON'T SEEM VERY HAPPY ABOUT IT.

LAST WEEK I'D HAVE GIVEN ANYTHING TO MEET SOMEONE LIKE YOU. NOW...

OKAY, FIRST OF ALL... WOW. SECOND... YOU AND I ARE HAVING DINNER TONIGHT. GOT IT? IT'S OBVIOUS YOU NEED SOMEONE TO TALK TO AND I'M A GOOD LISTENER. WHAT'S YOUR NAME?

MARK.

HI MARK. I'M ALEX.

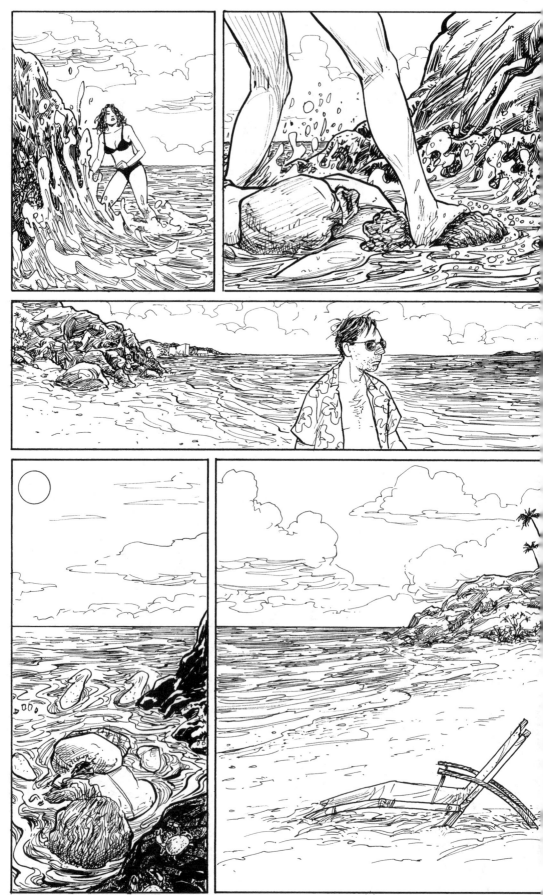

MALIBU, CALIFORNIA.

BEEP! BEEP!

CLICK!

THE BOSS ISN'T GOING TO LIKE THIS.

AND I'M THE ONE WHO HAS TO TELL HER.

ARE THEY SURE IT'S PIPER?

HOW LONG WAS SHE IN THE WATER?

NOT LONG ENOUGH.

13

DETECTIVE... THANKS FOR THE CALL. WE APPRECIATE IT.

YOU TWO PARKER GIRLS?

THERE'S NO SUCH THING AS PARKER GIRLS.

RIIIGHT.

≥Sigh≥

SO PIPER MAY WAS ONE OF YOURS?

JUST A FRIEND.

A FRIEND MARRIED TO A BILLIONAIRE.

WHICH MAKES SENSE — YOU PEOPLE WANTING TO KEEP AN EYE ON ZACKARY MAY...

ONE OF THE RICHEST MEN IN AMERICA.

YOU KNOW THIS IS GOING TO BLOW UP BIG, RIGHT? FAMOUS ACTRESS WASHES UP DEAD ON THE BEACH IN MALIBU... THE PRESS WILL NEVER LET IT GO. THEY'LL DIG UP EVERY TURD SHE DROPPED AND PRINT IT.

ANYTHING I SHOULD KNOW BEFORE THEY DO, MISS UH... SORRY, I DIDN'T CATCH YOUR NAME.

15

=PHEW!=

BZZT! BZZT!

CHERRY... YOU'RE UP EARLY.

BOSS, PIPER MAY IS DEAD. HER BODY WASHED UP ON MALIBU BEACH THIS MORNING, BECKY AND I CONFIRMED IT.

SHE DROWNED?

YES, BUT THERE'S BLOOD IN HER EAR. SHE WAS UNCONSCIOUS WHEN SHE ENTERED THE WATER.

WHAT IS SHE WEARING?

BIKINI AND A COVER-UP.

SO SHE WAS PROBABLY ON A BOAT YESTERDAY, STAY ON IT, THE FIRST 24 IS WHEN THE LIES ARE RAW.

GOT IT.

TAMBI... WHAT HAPPENED?

PIPER MAY IS DEAD.

OH NO. SHE'S SO CUTE!

SHE WAS.

AND SHE MONITORED ZACKARY MAY FOR ME, HE BETTER HAVE A HELL OF AN ALIBI.

I'M A CPA FOR A LARGE FIRM. IT WAS EASY.

TO BORROW MONEY?

UH HUH.

I MEAN, THEY DON'T KNOW ABOUT IT YET, BUT...

YEAH.

OH.

IF YOU DON'T MIND ME ASKING, HOW MUCH DID YOU... BORROW?

TEN MILLION DOLLARS.

SPIT!

CHAMPAGNE!

YOU, MY FRIEND, HAVE BALLS!

I SALUTE YOU, SIR, AND YOUR ORBS OF STEEL!

18

SO WHY THE LONG FACE? ENJOY YOURSELF WHILE YOU CAN, LIVE IT UP.

THE DOCTOR'S OFFICE CALLED ME MONDAY. THERE WAS A MIX-UP WITH THE TESTS, I'M FINE.

I DON'T HAVE CANCER.

THAT'S GREAT! NOW YOU CAN DO ALL...

WAIT FOR IT.

OH SHIT.

THERE IT IS.

YEAH.

≈SQUEAK!≈

≈SIGH≈

NEVER MIND.

TAKE IT AWAY.

CAN YOU PUT THE MONEY BACK? YOU SAID THEY DON'T KNOW YET.

IT'S NOT THAT EASY. THE MONEY WAS FOR MY SISTER. SHE'S A WIDOW WITH THREE LITTLE KIDS, THAT MONEY WOULD GIVE THEM SECURITY AND AN EDUCATION.

OH.

SHE THINKS IT'S MY LIFE INSURANCE, I CAN'T GO BACK ON MY WORD, I WON'T! BUT IT'S JUST A MATTER OF TIME BEFORE THE FIRM DISCOVERS THE MONEY'S GONE, THEY'LL FIND ME, I'LL GO TO PRISON AND THEY'LL TAKE THE MONEY BACK.

AND YOU'RE NOT MADE FOR PRISON LIFE, MARK. YOUR BUTT'S TOO SMALL. YOU'LL BE CRIPPLED FOR LIFE.

OH GOD.

SERIOUSLY, YOU'LL HAVE TO WEAR ADULT DIAPERS.

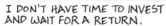
WHINE!

HEY, I'VE GOT AN IDEA... WHY DON'T YOU USE THE TEN TO MAKE ANOTHER TEN? THEN YOU CAN REPLACE THE "LOAN" AND PAY YOUR SISTER!

I DON'T HAVE TIME TO INVEST AND WAIT FOR A RETURN.

YOU DON'T HAVE AN HOUR?

WHAT?

ASK ME WHAT I DO FOR A LIVING.

WHAT DO YOU...

CRYPTO CURRENCY EXCHANGE.

THAT'S A SHIT SHOW!

YES, WHICH IS WHY IT WORKS. I CAN DOUBLE YOUR MONEY OVERNIGHT.

BULL!

MARK, WHERE DO YOU THINK ALL THE NEW BILLIONAIRES ARE COMING FROM... HEDGE FUNDS? HITCH A RIDE ON AN INTERNATIONAL ARMS DEAL, DUDE. WATCH IT BOUNCE AROUND AND CASH OUT AT TWENTY. IT'S ILLEGAL AS HELL BUT IT WORKS!

TELL YOU WHAT. LETS GRAB SOME CHAMPAGNE, GO TO YOUR ROOM AND TEST IT WITH ONE MILLION. IF I DON'T DOUBLE IT IN THIRTY MINUTES I'LL PULL YOUR ONE OUT AND ANYTHING ELSE YOU LIKE PULLED. IF IT WORKS, WE GO THE WHOLE TEN AND SCREW OUR BRAINS OUT UNTIL IT'S TWENTY.

DEAL?

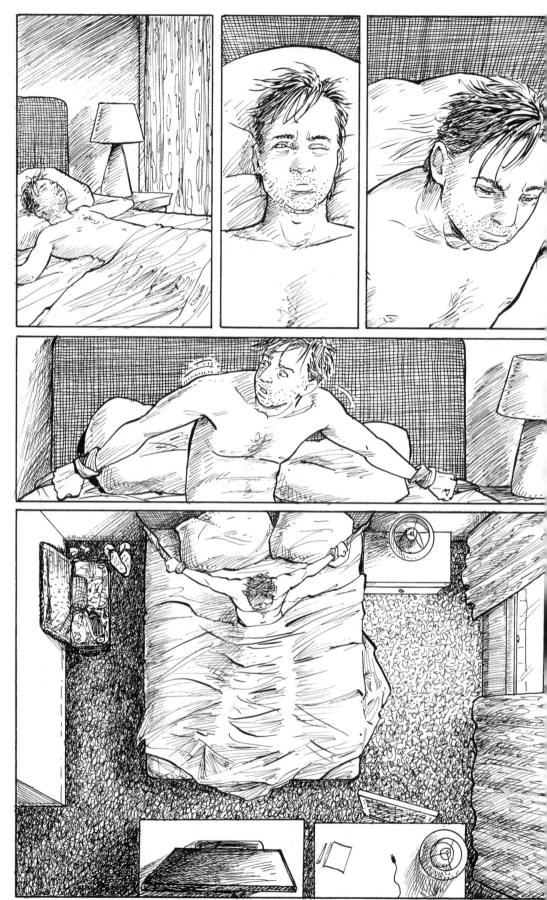

You are free to choose, but you are not free
from the consequences of your choice.
—Zig Ziglar

WHIIIRRR VROOM

IMPRESSIVE, ISN'T IT?

VERY. DID YOU MAKE IT?

ME? NAW... BUT THANKS FOR THINKING I COULD.

I'VE LEARNED TO NEVER UNDERESTIMATE YOU, CHOOVANSKI. YOU CAN DO ANYTHING YOU SET YOUR MIND TO.

THANKS, SIS, IT'S GOOD TO SEE YOU AGAIN.

SO YEAH, FRANCINE DATED A SCULPTOR IN COLLEGE. HE MADE THAT ON HIS OWN AND ENTERED IT IN THE SCHOOL'S ART EXHIBIT.

ON HIS OWN?

SHE DIDN'T KNOW.

WHEN FRANCINE FOUND OUT SHE WAS MORTIFIED. I DON'T KNOW IF YOU'VE EVER SEEN HER MAD BUT...

OH YEAH!

HAWAII. THAT TIME I CAME TO GET YOU FOR RUSSIA.

SLAP!

SO ANYWAY, I TRACKED THE GUY DOWN AND MADE HIM AN OFFER HE COULDN'T REFUSE. HOME AT LAST.

IS FRANCINE HERE IN SANTA FE WITH YOU?

NO. SHE TOOK THE KIDS TO VISIT HER BROTHER PETER AND HIS FAMILY IN FLORIDA.

GOOD.

CLANK!

REMEMBER THE GEEK WHO USED TO COME TO DARCY PARKER'S PARTIES AND ALWAYS ASKED FOR YOU?

ZACK MAY.

I REMEMBER EVERY BODY I HAD TO BE WITH AT DARCY'S.

EVERY.

SINGLE.

BODY.

YOU KNEW HIM BEFORE HE BECAME A TECH GIANT, DID HE EVER MENTION SATELLITES OR WORKING WITH THE CHINESE?

I DON'T KNOW, MAYBE.

IT'S HARD TO UNDER-STAND THEM WHEN YOU'RE SITTING ON THEIR FACE.

THAT ANGER IS ALWAYS THERE, ISN'T IT? JUST BENEATH THE SURFACE.

HOW WOULD YOU LIKE A LITTLE PAY BACK?

YOU'RE THE CAPTAIN OF ZACKARY MAY'S YACHT WHEN IT GOES OUT AND IT WAS COMING BACK FROM CATALINA THE NIGHT PIPER DIED, WHAT HAPPENED OUT THERE ON THE BOAT THAT NIGHT?

I'M NOT TELLING YOU SQUAT, LADY! WHO DO YOU THINK YOU ARE?!

I'M THE ONE PERSON YOU DO TELL, BOB. YOU CAN SAY WHATEVER YOU WANT TO THE POLICE BUT YOU'RE GOING TO TELL ME EVERYTHING THAT HAPPENED THAT NIGHT AND WHAT THEY SAID.

CLICK!

AND IF I DON'T?

THEN BECKY IS GOING TO SHOOT YOUR DICK OFF.

MR MAY, I'M SO SORRY! I PROMISE I WILL REPAY EVERY PENNY, I SWEAR!

IT'S NOT ABOUT THE MONEY — IT'S ABOUT THE ACCOUNT YOU STOLE IT FROM.

THE CAYMAN ACCOUNT? IT'S NOT ON THE BOOKS. NO ONE WILL EVER KNOW!

YOUR WITHDRAWALS EXPOSE THE ACCOUNT TO ANY FUTURE FORENSIC AUDIT. YOUR STUPIDITY LEAVES ME WITH A BILLION DOLLAR MESS TO CLEAN UP.

I KNOW I SCREWED UP BUT I WANT TO MAKE IT RIGHT. I CAN FIX THIS!

HOW? YOU SLEPT WITH MY WIFE. YOU CAN'T FIX THAT. NOW SHE'S DEAD, YOU CAN'T FIX THAT. YOU COMPROMISED MY PRIVATE BANKING — THAT CAN'T BE UNDONE — AND YOU STOLE FROM ME. YOU CAN'T RETURN THE MONEY BECAUSE I ALREADY HAVE IT. I HAD TO HIRE THE PARKER GIRLS TO FIND YOU AND GET IT BACK BUT I GOT IT. THAT ALONE COST ME MORE THAN YOU WOULD MAKE IN A LIFETIME. THE PARKER GIRLS ARE NOT INEXPENSIVE!

PIPER'S DEAD?

YOU HAVEN'T HEARD? SHE DRANK HERSELF INTO A STUPOR WHEN YOU LEFT AND FELL OFF THE BOAT. SHE WAS NEVER A GOOD SWIMMER.

JESUS!

YOU KILLED HER! AND NOW YOU'RE GOING TO KILL ME, TOO!

I DON'T KILL PEOPLE, MR HARRIS. I LET THEM KILL THEMSELVES.

NO! WAIT!

SORRY. I HAVE A PLANE TO CATCH.

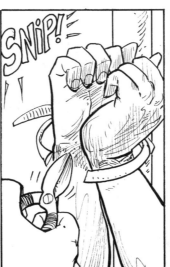

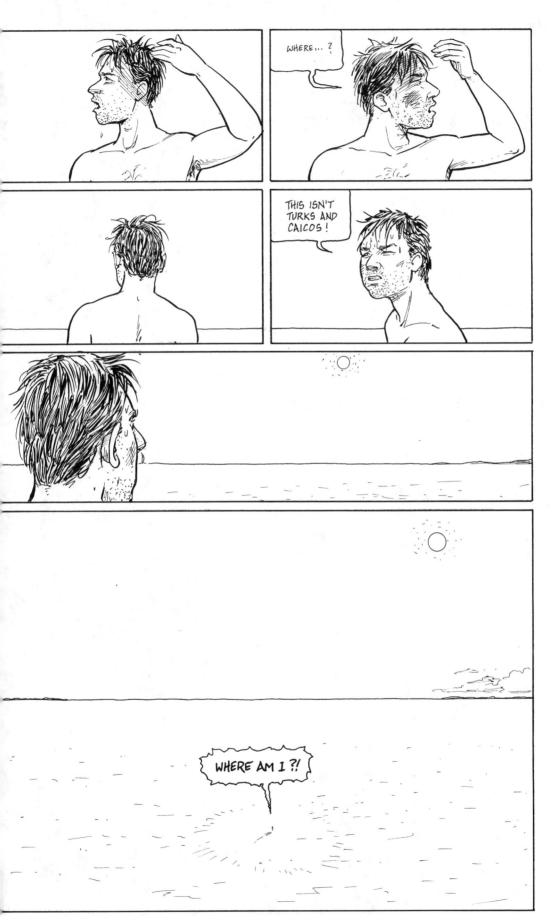

At night I go on board and say Good-night
To all my friends on shore;
I shut my eyes and sail away
And see and hear no more.
—Robert Louis Stevenson

"ZACKARY MAY IS NOT A WARM AND FUZZY PERSON."

"I GUESS YOU DON'T HAVE TO BE WHEN YOU'RE A BILLIONAIRE."

"BUT I KNOW HE WAS CRAZY ABOUT PIPER..."

"AND SHE HAD A WAY OF MAKING HIM SMILE AND RELAX A LITTLE. I NEVER SAW ANYONE ELSE DO THAT— MAKE HIM SMILE."

"I THINK MR MAY WAS SURPRISED THAT PIPER AGREED TO MARRY HIM. FRANKLY, SHE WAS OUT OF HIS LEAGUE, IF YOU KNOW WHAT I MEAN."

" BUT SHE SEEMED TO LIKE HIM WELL ENOUGH AND THEY SPENT A LOT OF TIME TOGETHER."

"IT MUST BE HARD, YEAH? NOT KNOWING WHO YOU CAN TRUST AND WHO JUST WANTS YOUR MONEY. I GET THAT."

" BUT I HAVE TO SAY I NEVER HEARD THEM TALK ABOUT MONEY. AND I NEVER HEARD HER ASK HIM TO BUY HER SOMETHING."

"NOW, I DID HEAR THEM ARGUE ABOUT HER MEN FRIENDS."

"MR. MAY WAS A JEALOUS MAN."

" BECAUSE, YOU KNOW, WITH PIPER BEING AN ACTRESS AND ALL, HER FRIENDS WERE ALL ACTORS AND MODELS, TOO, RIGHT? HANDSOME AND FRIENDLY... EVERY- THING MAY WAS NOT."

" OH THAT GOT UNDER HIS SKIN. AND THE NICER THOSE GUYS WERE TO HIM THE MADDER MAY GOT."

" HE DIDN'T SAY ANYTHING AT FIRST BUT I WAS WATCHING THIS GO ON ALL THE TIME."

" EITHER PIPER DIDN'T SEE IT OR SHE DIDN'T CARE."

" BUT IT ALL CAME TO A HEAD THAT WEEKEND IN CATALINA,"

" PIPER WAS MAKING A MOVIE AND SHE INVITED HER CO-STAR TO JOIN THEM SO THEY COULD GO OVER THEIR LINES TOGETHER."

" SATURDAY, ALL THEY DID WAS DRINK AND FLIRT, RIGHT IN FRONT OF MAY."

"AND HE WAS NOT HAPPY ABOUT IT."

"THEY SAID TERRIBLE THINGS TO EACH OTHER THAT DAY. THE KIND OF THINGS YOU CAN'T TAKE BACK LATER."

"YOU COULD TELL THERE WAS NO SAVING THE MARRIAGE."

"IT WAS OVER."

"I TURNED THE SHIP OVER TO THE FIRST MATE AND WENT TO MY QUARTERS AT MIDNIGHT. A FEW MINUTES LATER I HEARD MR. MAY GO TO HIS CABIN AND SLAM THE DOOR. IT SOUNDED LIKE PIPER THREW SOMETHING AT THE DOOR THEN SHOUTED 'YOU BASTARD'. I HEARD HER STOMP UP THE STAIRS AND AFTER THAT IT WAS QUIET. I TURNED OUT THE LIGHT AND WENT TO SLEEP. PEACE AT LAST."

"I ASSUMED SHE WAS GOING TO SLEEP IN ONE OF THE GUEST CABINS OR ON DECK."

"BUT IT WAS CHILLY OUT AND FOG WAS ROLLING IN."

THE REST OF THE NIGHT WAS QUIET.

IN THE MORNING, MR. MAY AND HIS GUEST TOOK BREAKFAST IN THEIR CABINS. IT WAS ABOUT 9:15 WHEN THE CHIEF STEWARD INFORMED ME THAT MRS MAY COULD NOT BE FOUND.

WE SEARCHED EVERY INCH OF THE SHIP. SHE WAS NOT ONBOARD. WE DID FIND DROPS OF BLOOD ON THE STEPS BY THE DINGHY. IT LOOKED LIKE SHE HAD TRIED TO LOWER IT INTO THE WATER..., BUT SLIPPED AND FELL OVERBOARD.

I REPORTED THIS TO MR. MAY AND TOLD HIM I WAS CALLING THE COAST GUARD. WE WERE TALKING ABOUT IT WHEN HE RECEIVED A CALL INFORMING HIM THAT HIS WIFE'S BODY HAD WASHED ASHORE ON MALIBU BEACH.

HOW DID HE REACT?

WELL, YOU'VE SEEN HIM ON TV. MR MAY IS HARD TO READ.

ON THE SURFACE HE'S CALM.

WHAT'S BELOW IS ANYBODY'S GUESS.

THERE'S NOTHING MORE TO TELL YOU, REALLY. WE ANCHORED OFF CATALINA AND MR. MAY'S HELICOPTER CAME AND TOOK HIM BACK TO L.A.

THAT'S THE TRUTH AS I SAW IT, THAT'S WHAT I TOLD THE POLICE.

WHAT DID YOU HEAR TO MAKE YOU THINK THE MARRIAGE COULDN'T BE SAVED?

HE DIDN'T PAY ANY ATTENTION TO HER AND SHE DIDN'T RESPECT HIM.

YOU CAN'T FIX ANYTHING UNTIL YOU FIX THAT.

51

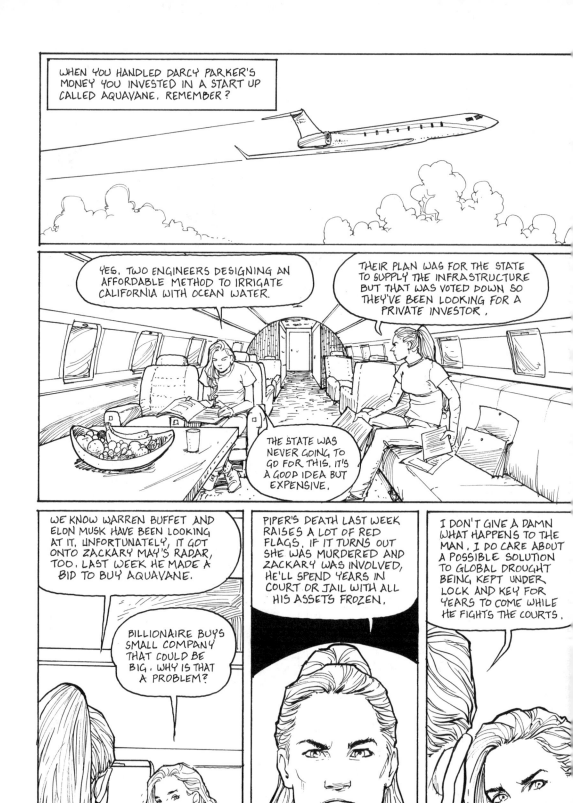

WHEN YOU HANDLED DARCY PARKER'S MONEY YOU INVESTED IN A START UP CALLED AQUAVANE, REMEMBER?

YES, TWO ENGINEERS DESIGNING AN AFFORDABLE METHOD TO IRRIGATE CALIFORNIA WITH OCEAN WATER.

THEIR PLAN WAS FOR THE STATE TO SUPPLY THE INFRASTRUCTURE BUT THAT WAS VOTED DOWN SO THEY'VE BEEN LOOKING FOR A PRIVATE INVESTOR.

THE STATE WAS NEVER GOING TO GO FOR THIS. IT'S A GOOD IDEA BUT EXPENSIVE.

WE KNOW WARREN BUFFET AND ELON MUSK HAVE BEEN LOOKING AT IT. UNFORTUNATELY, IT GOT ONTO ZACKARY MAY'S RADAR, TOO. LAST WEEK HE MADE A BID TO BUY AQUAVANE.

BILLIONAIRE BUYS SMALL COMPANY THAT COULD BE BIG. WHY IS THAT A PROBLEM?

PIPER'S DEATH LAST WEEK RAISES A LOT OF RED FLAGS. IF IT TURNS OUT SHE WAS MURDERED AND ZACKARY WAS INVOLVED, HE'LL SPEND YEARS IN COURT OR JAIL WITH ALL HIS ASSETS FROZEN.

I DON'T GIVE A DAMN WHAT HAPPENS TO THE MAN. I DO CARE ABOUT A POSSIBLE SOLUTION TO GLOBAL DROUGHT BEING KEPT UNDER LOCK AND KEY FOR YEARS TO COME WHILE HE FIGHTS THE COURTS.

AND THAT'S HOW I ENDED UP ON A PLANE TO L.A. WITH MY HALF-SISTER, KATINA CHOOVANSKI.

KATCHOO WAS A PARKER GIRL BACK IN THE DAY.

A DAMN GOOD ONE, I MIGHT ADD.

THE PARKER GIRLS.

THEY DON'T EXIST. THEY'RE A MYTH. THEY DON'T HAVE AN OFFICE OR A TAX I.D.

YOU DON'T SEE ONE COMING BUT YOU CAN TELL WHERE THEY'VE BEEN... WHEN A SUBPOENED POLITICIAN OR DISGRACED CEO CLAIMS A WOMAN WON THEIR TRUST AND LISTENED TO THEIR SECRET PROBLEMS THEN DISAPPEARED.

POWER. LEVERAGE. MONEY.

SECRETS ARE A BUSINESS.

AND BUSINESS IS GOOD.

IF I WANT TO KNOW YOUR SECRET I'LL BEAT IT OUT YOU.

BUT A PARKER GIRL CAN GET THE SAME INFORMATION OVER DINNER.

AND IF YOU'RE A BOUQUET OF BAD SHE'LL WRAP YOU IN LEGS AND SILK SHEETS UNTIL YOU HAVE NOTHING LEFT TO CONFESS.

PARKER GIRLS ARE VERY... VERY GOOD AT WHAT THEY DO.

OR SO I'M TOLD.

TRY TO PROVE IT.

QUESTION... IF THEY DECIDE PIPER'S DEATH WAS AN ACCIDENT, WILL YOU BE OKAY WITH MAY?

NO.

WHY NOT?

WHEN MAY AGREED TO PAY OUR FEE OF FIVE MILLION TO FIND THE CPA, I THOUGHT IT WAS ODD — SPENDING FIVE TO RECOVER TEN — IT DOESN'T MAKE SENSE

SO WHEN WE FOUND THE CPA IN TURKS AND CAICOS, I HAD OUR GIRL ON THE JOB TRANSFER THE MONEY TO SAFETY THEN BRING BACK HIS HARD DRIVE.

WE WERE ABLE TO LOOK AT THE ACCOUNT THE CPA EMBEZZLED FROM AND THE DEPOSITS WERE STUNNING. A BILLION DOLLARS IN TWO YEARS.

IS IT COMING FROM INSIDE THE COMPANY? LIKE, OVER-CHARGES AND PAYMENTS TO PHANTOM BRANCHES?

NO.

IT'S ALL WIRE TRANSFERS FROM A HONG KONG BANK THE CHINESE GOVERNMENT USES FOR INTERNATIONAL BUSINESS TRANSACTIONS.

MAY'S COMPUTER TECHNOLOGY IS A GLOBAL BUSINESS. MAYBE IT'S ALL LEGIT BUT CLIENT DISCRETE.

WE CHECKED. EVERY DEPOSIT COINCIDES WITH AN UPDATE ON THE LIGHT CHIP MAY'S DEVELOPING FOR U.S. SATELLITES.

THAT'S REAL? I THOUGHT LIGHT BEAM TECH WAS A THEORY.

MAY SAYS HE'LL HAVE ONE IN PRODUCTION BY THE END OF THE YEAR. IT SHOULD GIVE US A SIGNIFICANT ADVANTAGE... BUT NOT IF THE CHINESE HAVE IT, TOO.

OKAY SO WHAT DO YOU WANT TO DO HERE? YOU'VE GOT THIS GUY DOWN FOR EVERYTHING FROM MURDER TO ESPIONAGE. IF HE'S THAT BAD JUST KILL HIM.

AND SAVE HIM FROM ALL THE DISGRACE AND JAIL TIME COMING HIS WAY? NO, I WANT TO WATCH HIS SPECTACULAR FALL FROM POWER. WHAT I DON'T WANT IS FOR HIM TO TAKE AQUAVANE DOWN WITH HIM.

MAY IS A BLIP IN HISTORY. AQUAVANE COULD CHANGE HISTORY.

MAY NEEDS TO STEP AWAY FROM AQUAVANE. LEAVE IT ALONE SO A GOOD INVESTOR CAN BE FOUND. THAT'S WHERE YOU COME IN.

I DON'T KNOW ANYTHING ABOUT INVESTORS, TAMBI.

I'LL FIND THE INVESTOR. I NEED YOU TO CONVINCE MAY TO DROP HIS BID FOR AQUAVANE.

WHY DO YOU THINK I COULD TALK HIM OUT OF IT?

BECAUSE HE LIKES YOU. YOU'LL BE ABLE TO GET CLOSE AND TALK TO HIM IN CONFIDENCE.

AND I KNOW YOU, CHOOVANSKI. ONCE YOU'RE IN THAT MAN'S HEAD YOU'LL MAKE AQUAVANE LOOK LIKE A BOMB HE CAN'T GET RID OF FAST ENOUGH.

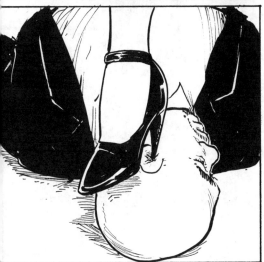

Terry Moore

PARKER GIRLS

ABSTRACT STUDIO

4

Even now I think about you,
In the middle of the night;
And I can't believe it still
Can hurt so bad.

—Barry Manilow

SOMETHING MADE A HALF INCH DEPRESSION IN HER SKULL.

THAT COULD BE ANYTHING FROM A FALL TO A GOLF CLUB, WITH NO DEFENSE MARKS I THINK SHE DIDN'T KNOW WHAT HIT HER.

AND IF THERE'S A MURDER WEAPON, YOU KNOW IT'S ON THE OCEAN FLOOR NOW.

SO, WHO'S MISSING A GOLF CLUB?

OR HAMMER?

YOUR WEAPON OF CHOICE.

WELL PIPER HAS TOLD US ALL SHE CAN, THE BOAT CAPTAIN TOLD US WHAT HE KNOWS. THAT LEAVES THE ACTOR...

JOHN B.

ANGELA SAYS HE'S BOOKED TO FLY TO TORONTO TOMORROW TO RESUME WORK ON THE MOVIE HE WAS SHOOTING WITH PIPER.

I'M NOT SURPRISED.

THE ROADS MUST ROLL, YEAH?

HOWLIN' WOLF?

HEINLEIN.

HMM.

YOU WANT TO GO SEE MR. B?

YES.

IT'S TWO IN THE MORNING.

YEP.

HE'S NOT GOING TO BE HAPPY.

NOPE.

I LOVE MY JOB.

THE EASIEST THING WOULD BE TO KNOCK ON THE DOOR.

WHERE'S THE FUN IN THAT?

LET'S GO.

NO SIGN OF PERSONNEL.

I SEE CAMERAS. MOTION DETECTORS. PROBABLY A PERIMETER BEAM AND REMOTE MONITORING.

START THE SCRAMBLER. I'LL GET THE POWER BOX.

WHAT DO YOU WANT?!

TELL ME WHAT HAPPENED THE NIGHT PIPER DIED.

I DON'T KNOW. AFTER DINNER I STAYED IN MY ROOM ALL NIGHT.

WHY?

BECAUSE THEY WERE FIGHTING! DINNER WAS A NIGHTMARE! I TOOK MY DESSERT TO MY ROOM AND STAYED THERE. I TURNED UP THE TV SO I WOULDN'T HAVE TO LISTEN TO THEM!

IF I COULD HAVE CALLED AN UBER I WOULD HAVE!

ARE YOU FROM THE STUDIO? I PROMISE YOU, I DIDN'T DO ANYTHING WRONG. PLEASE DON'T FIRE ME!

TELL ME THE TRUTH SO WE CAN HELP YOU, JOHN. WHAT WERE PIPER AND ZACKARY FIGHTING ABOUT?

EVERYTHING! THEY FOUGHT ABOUT EVERY-THING WRONG WITH HIM AND EVERYTHING WRONG WITH HER! AND BELIEVE ME, SHE WAS OVER IT! SHE WANTED A DIVORCE!

SO THEY YELLED ABOUT THAT FOR AWHILE, THEN I HEARD HIM STOMP TO HIS ROOM AND SLAM THE DOOR. THEN SHE SLAMMED A DOOR AND IT WAS QUIET.

THE NEXT MORNING I HEARD VOICES AND BOATS COMING AND GOING. ZACK AND PIPER WERE GONE. I RODE BACK ON THE YACHT AND HEARD ABOUT PIPER ON THE INTERNET.

PIPER MAY DEAD!
BODY FOUND ON BEACH!

I'M NOT GOING TO GET CANCELLED FOR BEING THERE, AM I?

WHAT DID THEY BOTH SAY?

HMM?

YOU WERE SAYING YOU FOUND IT ODD THAT BOTH JOHN AND THE CAPTAIN SAID...

OH, YEAH. THEY BOTH SAID THEY HEARD TWO DOORS SLAM BUT NEITHER ONE OF THEM SAW IT HAPPEN. THEY JUST ASSUMED IT WAS THE SOUND OF DOORS.

THEY HEARD FIGHTING THEN SLAM, SLAM... THEN SILENCE.

WHAT IF IT WASN'T DOORS?

BUT DON'T YOU THINK THE CAPTAIN WOULD KNOW THAT SOUND?

HE'S A RENT-A-PILOT. IT'S NOT HIS BOAT. IF WE GOT HIM BACK ON BOARD AND SLAMMED THE CABIN DOORS I WONDER IF IT WOULD BE THE SOUND HE HEARD.

75

77

I'm here for a couple of days if you want to have a drink. Catch up.

I'd like that very much.

Call me.

I couldn't help but notice you're still not wearing any underwear.

Remember that during your speech.

EXCUSE ME....

JIM LEHMAN, MR MAY'S PERSONAL SECRETARY. IF YOU DON'T MIND MY ASKING.... WHO ARE YOU?

GRETA VAN FLEET, DEPARTMENT OF JUSTICE. DON'T SAY OR DO ANYTHING TO INTERFERE WITH THIS INVESTIGATION, JIM, OR YOU COULD SPEND THE NEXT 30 YEARS IN JAIL.

HUH.

WHAT ARE YOU DOING?!

IT'S STUCK.

SQUISH! POP!

SQUASH! CRUNCH!

SPLORT!

LOOK WHAT YOU'VE DONE!

YEAH, BROKE THE HEEL CAP OFF.

NO! YOU KILLED HIM! IT COST ME 50 GRAND TO BUY OUT HIS UFC CONTRACT! YOU OWE ME $50,000, YOU PSYCHOPATH!

HE RUINED MY SHOES! WE'RE EVEN!

YOUR SHOES ARE NOT WORTH $50,000!

WANNA BET?! CHRISTIAN LOUBOUTINS ARE NOT CHEAP, NIKOLA!

SLIT!

WHAT KIND OF AN IDIOT PAYS FIFTY K FOR A PAIR OF SHOES?!

YOU DID. JUST NOW.

SO ARE WE GETTING MARRIED IN APRIL OR...?

THE WEDDING'S OFF, ASSHOLE.

MY FATHER'S NOT GOING TO LIKE THIS!

YOU'LL BE GETTING A VERY STERN LETTER FROM OUR ATTORNEY!

I WANT BACK THE JEWELRY I GAVE YOU! AND THE CAR!

AND THOSE SHOES! THOSE ARE MY SHOES!

81

BZZT!
BZZT!

BZZZT!
BZZT!

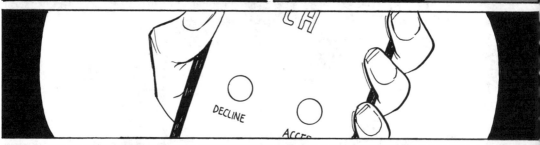
DECLINE

ACCE

HI CHERRY.

KELLY, YOU WORKING?

YEAH, BUT I'M READY FOR A BREAK. WHAT'S UP?

SQUEAK!

I'M WORKING ON PIPER'S DEATH AND I NEED YOUR TALENTS ON SOMETHING.

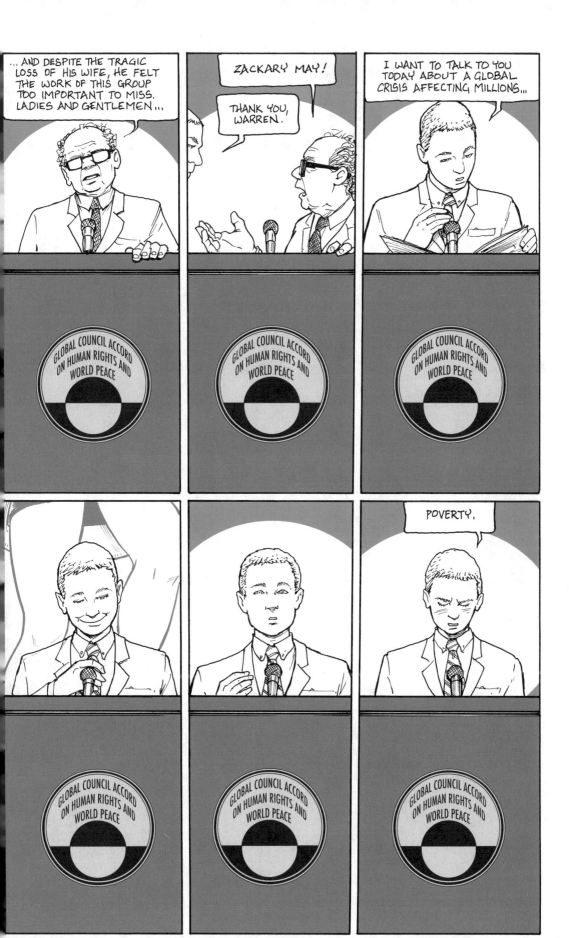

83

"To the last, I grapple with thee;
From Hell's heart, I stab at thee;
For hate's sake,
I spit my last breath at thee."

—Herman Melville

SO BOB TOLD ME YOU'RE PRIVATE INVESTIGATORS.

THAT'S RIGHT.

AND I SHOULD LET YOU SEE THE MAY'S BOAT... LOOK AROUND.

DO YOU WORK FOR MR. MAY?

PEOPLE WHO WORK FOR MR. MAY ARE NOT ALLOWED TO TELL YOU THEY WORK FOR MR. MAY.

FAIR ENOUGH,

YOU SAY YOU WANT TO SEE THE CABINS?

I WANT TO SEE MR. MAY'S BEDROOM, THEN THE GUEST ROOMS.

THIS IS THE MAIN SUITE WHERE THE MAYS SLEEP.

UH...SLEPT.

BECKY?

GOT YOUR SIX.

THE DOOR'S HYDRAULIC.

YEP. YOU PUT YOUR HAND IN THE SLOT AND IT OPENS THE DOOR.

AND RECORDS THE PRINTS?

WE'RE NOT SUPPOSED TO ADMIT THAT BUT ...YEAH.

OPEN IT.

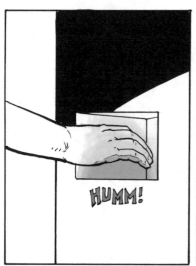

HUMM!

SSSHHHHHHHT!

LIKE THE ENTERPRISE.

CAN YOU OPERATE THIS DOOR MANUALLY AND SLAM IT SHUT?

MANUAL, YES. JUST TURN IT OFF WITH THE FIREMAN'S KEY.

SLAM IT?

YOU'D HAVE TO TAKE THE PANEL OFF, DISCONNECT THE HYDRAULICS. THIS PANEL'S NEVER BEEN OFF.

HOW DO YOU KNOW?

THE FACTORY SEAL'S NEVER BEEN BROKEN.

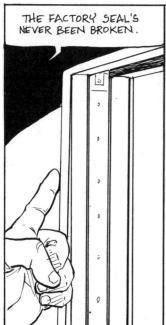

DO THE OTHER BEDROOMS HAVE A DOOR LIKE THIS?

YES.

ARE THEY SEALED?

YES.

≥SIGH≤

THE LOUNGE WHERE THEY EAT AND HAVE DRINKS... ENTERTAIN GUESTS.

OBVIOUSLY EVERYTHING IS STOWED AWAY WHILE THEY'RE AWAY BUT WHEN THEY TAKE THE BOAT OUT THIS ROOM IS DECKED OUT, FULL BAR, TV, FLOWERS...

WHEN THE BOAT CAME BACK FROM THE CATALINA TRIP, WAS ANYTHING DAMAGED OR MISSING? FURNITURE, WINDOWS, WALLS? I MEAN, THIS ROOM IN PARTICULAR.

NO. EVERYTHING LOOKED FINE.

WOULD YOU BE ABLE TO TELL IF SOMETHING WAS REPAIRED OR REPLACED WHILE THE BOAT WAS OUT?

THEY'D CALL ME ABOUT IT AND I DIDN'T GET A CALL LIKE THAT.

LOOK, SHE'S MAKING ME NERVOUS WATCHING ME LIKE THAT. IS IT REALLY NECESSARY? IT'S RUDE!

SORRY. YOU CAN GO. I WANT TO LOOK AROUND HERE FOR A MINUTE.

I DON'T KNOW WHY YOU FEEL THE NEED TO DO THAT. I'M JUST AN EMPLOYEE, OKAY?

THANK YOU.

NOT MY BOAT, NOT MY PROBLEM.

MOST ILLOGICAL.

IT'S THIS SHIP.

WHAT'S WITH YOU AND STAR TREK ALL OF A SUDDEN?

I'VE NEVER SEEN ANYTHING LIKE THIS BEFORE.

IT'S JUST A BOAT, BECKY.

A VERY...

VERY...

EXPENSIVE BOAT.

SO THE LAST PLACE PIPER WAS SEEN ALIVE WAS IN THIS ROOM.

THE CAPTAIN AND JOHN B. HEARD WHAT THEY THOUGHT WERE SLAMMING DOORS.

BUT THESE DOORS DON'T SLAM.

AND NOW THE ROOM IS EMPTY SO WE DON'T KNOW WHAT WAS IN HERE THAT COULD HAVE MADE THAT SOUND.

WE KNOW THERE WERE TWO ANGRY PEOPLE.

IF ONE SHOVED THE OTHER AGAINST THE WALL...

SOMETHING LIKE THAT?

YES. BECKY... THAT WAS AWESOME!

THREE YEARS OF VASSAR LACROSSE, BABY.

SLAY.

SO MAY AND PIPER ARE IN HERE ARGUING WHEN MAY LOSES IT AND SHOVES PIPER AGAINST THE WALL SO HARD THIS THING SLAMS AND BOUNCES ON THE MOUNTING PLATE. PIPER'S OUT COLD AND MAY DECIDES IT'S A GOOD IDEA TO THROW HIS WIFE OVERBOARD. CUT TO BODY ON BEACH.

THAT DOESN'T EXPLAIN THE HOLE IN HER SKULL OR THE FACT THAT SHE WAS DEAD WHEN HER BODY HIT THE WATER. REMEMBER THE POST MORTEM... SHE DIDN'T DROWN.

HITTING THIS WALL WOULDN'T DO IT. HURT HER? YES. KNOCK A HOLE IN HER SKULL, KILLING HER INSTANTLY?

NO.

LET'S WALK THROUGH IT. HE THROWS PIPER AGAINST THE WALL SO HARD IT ROCKS THE TV. MAYBE IT KNOCKS THE BREATH OUT OF HER.

HE GRABS HER AGAIN.

SHE'S IN DANGER. AND SHE KNOWS IT.

SHE TRIES TO RUN.

AND THE NEAREST EXIT IS...

THAT SIDE DOOR IS CLOSER THAN THE MAIN ENTRY.

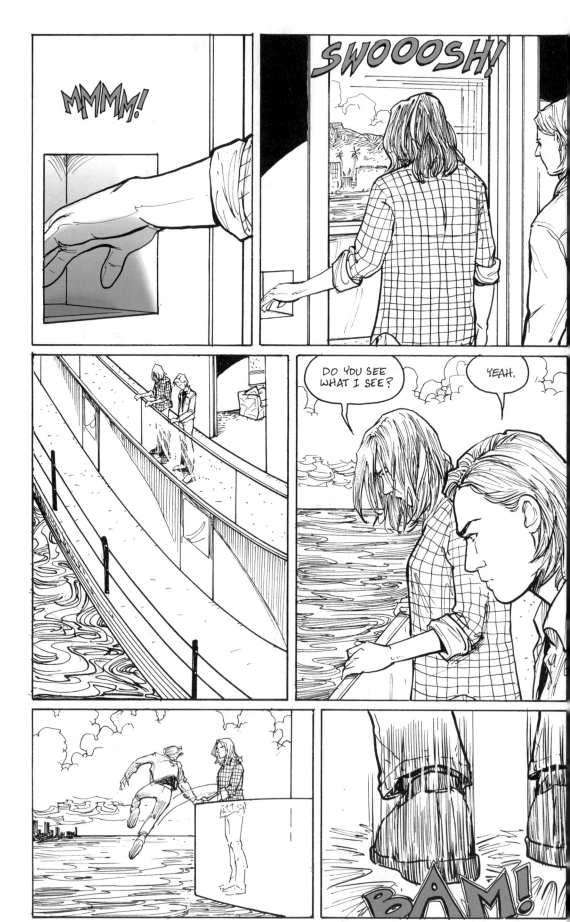

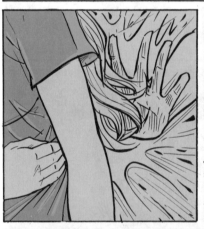

MMMM! SWOOOSH!

THUMP!

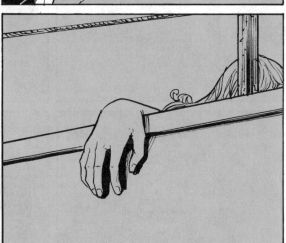

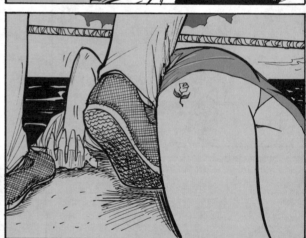

SPLASH!

I'M GOING TO KILL HIM.

MAYBE.

THAT'S UP TO THE BOSS TO DECIDE.

WHEN HE ATTACKED PIPER HE ATTACKED ALL OF US.

ALL I KNOW IS THE BOSS BROUGHT IN THE BIG GUNS TO DEAL WITH HIM.

WHO DID SHE GET?

CHOOVANSKI.

JESUS. SO THEY'RE GOING TO TAKE DOWN THE WHOLE EMPIRE?

MAYBE.

100

DING!

UNKNOWN

HI. ARE YOU FREE FOR THAT DRINK?

ANYTIME.

MY SECURITY WILL PICK YOU UP IN 5 MINUTES.

FLUSH

TIGER

BZZT! BZZZT!

KATCHOO, DON'T MEET WITH MAY. CHERRY SAYS HE KILLED PIPER IN COLD BLOOD. YOU'RE NOT SAFE.

STAY PUT, I'LL BE THERE IN TEN MINUTES AND WE'LL RE-GROUP. NOW THAT WE KNOW HE'S VIOLENT I DON'T WANT YOU ANYWHERE NEAR HIM!

I HAVE A GIRL WHO SPECIALIZES IN PSYCHOS. WE'LL CALL HER IN TO DO THIS.

CALL ME WHEN YOU GET THIS MESSAGE.

TIGER

KNOCK! KNOCK! KNOCK!

JUST A MINUTE.

Other books by Terry Moore

Strangers In Paradise

Echo

Rachel Rising

Motor Girl

Strangers In Paradise XXV

Five Years

Ever

Serial